Skunks in trunks

WATER PARK
ENTRANCE

Russell Punter

Illustrated by David Semple

On a warm, sunny day,
five lively young skunks

run into the Water Park,
dressed in bright trunks.

They dash with a splash
through the tiny tots' pools.

The tots get a soaking.

They zoom down so fast,
Lion shoots off the side.

They spin down Snake River.

Let's make it a race!

Their inflatable rings

bounce

all over

the place.

They dive in
the Pipe Ride.

Next moment,
they're stuck!

Mole and Crow want a turn.
But they're both out of luck.

"We're sorry," they mumble.

The rope bridge has broken.

"They can't swim at all!"

"Hold on!" yell the skunks.
"We're coming to get you!"

The friends plunge in bravely
and swim to the rescue.

They reach each pup quickly.

You've nothing to fear.

Now the manager's pleased
and she's had an idea...

Soon the Park has five lifeguards who help out each day.

When the Park shuts its doors,
they can stay on and play.

About phonics

Phonics is a method of teaching reading which is used extensively in today's schools. At its heart is an emphasis on identifying the *sounds* of letters, or combinations of letters, that are then put together to make words. These sounds are known as phonemes.

Starting to read

Learning to read is an important milestone for any child. The process can begin well before children start to learn letters and put them together to read words. The sooner children can discover books and enjoy stories and language, the better they will be prepared for reading themselves, first with the help of an adult and then independently.

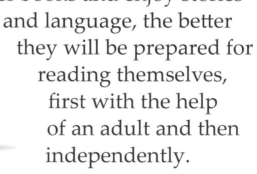

You can find out more about phonics on the Usborne Very First Reading website, **usborne.com/veryfirstreading** (US readers go to **veryfirstreading.com**). Click on the **Parents** tab at the top of the page, then scroll down and click on **About synthetic phonics**.

Phonemic awareness

An important early stage in pre-reading and early reading is developing phonemic awareness: that is, listening out for the sounds within words. Rhymes, rhyming stories and alliteration are excellent ways of encouraging phonemic awareness.

In this story, your child will soon identify the *u* sound, as in **skunks** and **trunks**. Look out, too, for rhymes such as **dash** – **splash** and **slide** – **side**.

Hearing your child read

If your child is reading a story to you, don't rush to correct mistakes, but be ready to prompt or guide if he or she is struggling. Above all, do give plenty of praise and encouragement.

Edited by Jenny Tyler and Lesley Sims
Designed by Sam Whibley

Reading consultants: Alison Kelly and Anne Washtell